CW00866338

THE CELTS
COLOURING AND ACTIVITY BOOK

D. C. Perkins, B.A. (Hons.), M.Ed., Ph.D. (Wales).

Illustrations by Craig Hildrew

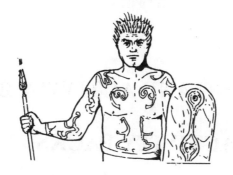

DOMINO BOOKS (WALES) LTD.,
P O Box 32,
Swansea SA1 1FN.

Typeset by Domino Books (Wales) Ltd
Printed in Hong Kong

ISBN 1 85772 052 0

COLOURING AND ACTIVITY BOOKS

ACTIVITY PACKS

We produce a range of these for Wales, the West Country and Scotland. Activity Packs can be customised for tourist venues, educational establishments, and historic houses. Please send for lists and details.

THIS COLOURING AND ACTIVITY BOOK BELONGS TO

NAME —————————————————————

ADDRESS ———————————————————

—————————————————————————

—————————————————————————

AGE ——————————————————————

CELTS

The name CELT comes from the word KELTOI used by the Greeks to describe savage tribes who lived north of the Alps. The arts, social customs and religious beliefs of these people suggest that they had a common cultural heritage.

The Celts were noted for their high spirits and they loved war and excitement. They were hospitable people who enjoyed feasting, drinking and quarrelling. Although regarded as a race they were, in reality, many tribes with a common cultural heritage. To name a few: there were the Belgae, the Canti, the Parisi, the Brigantes, the Iceni, the Dumnonii, the Durotriges and the Prythons (or *Brythons* who gave their name to this country in the word, *Britain*).

They were skilled in making weapons and other goods from iron and the tribes spread from north of the Alps into northern Italy, parts of Yugoslavia, Britain, France, Spain and even into central Europe. The Greeks and Romans came to fear these ferocious warriors in battle and described them as tall, fair and muscular. Militarily, they were almost unstoppable and controlled Europe from the 7th. century BC until they were conquered by the superior organisation and strength of Rome's Legions.

SOCIAL STRUCTURE
Socially, the Celts may be divided into five groups. These were

1. the King,
2. the Druids,
3. the Chieftains - the aristocratic and warrior class,
4. Freemen - mostly farmers,
5. Landless men and slaves.

THE CELTS - SOCIAL PYRAMID

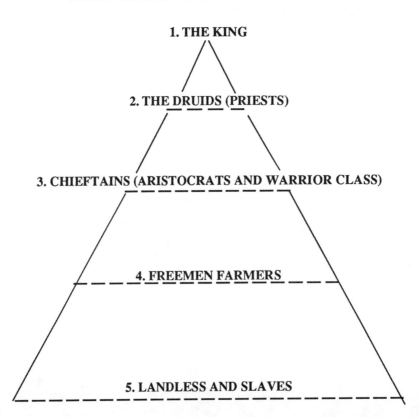

1. THE KING

2. THE DRUIDS (PRIESTS)

3. CHIEFTAINS (ARISTOCRATS AND WARRIOR CLASS)

4. FREEMEN FARMERS

5. LANDLESS AND SLAVES

Colour this picture of a Celtic Settlement using crayons or felt tipped pens.

CELTS

THE KING

The King was at the top of the social pyramid. He controlled a number of chieftains who were responsible for the areas under their command. Most decisions were made by the king but he took advice from the chieftains on political and military matters and he consulted the priests or druids on religious matters. The king was expected to be generous and a just ruler in times of peace, and a brave, decisive and successful leader in times of war. Whilst he had rights and duties towards his people, they had rights and duties towards him. [In this way Celtic society was similar to the way Europe was to be organised in later times, that is, the FEUDAL system in which all members of mediaeval society had rights and responsibilities to one another.]

THE DRUIDS

These priests were recruited from families of the chieftains but were treated as if they belonged to a higher social class. They were regarded with veneration, respect and a little fear by all classes and carried out magical and religious tasks. They favoured cutting off the heads of captured foes in ritual ceremonies and making sacrifices (including human ones) to please the gods. Druids consulted the omens (happenings or signs which they said predicted what would take place in the future such as the result of a battle) about all sorts of things. They advised the King when it was the best time to go to war and when it was wisest to make peace. They also said that going into combat naked gave the warriors magical protection. Druids could recite the tribe's history, religious rituals and the law. Nothing was written down and what they said was not questioned so they had considerable influence and power.

THE CHIEFTAINS

They controlled their own areas with the permission of the king. They advised the king, particularly in times of trouble and especially on political and military matters. They led their men into battle and also took part in duels, a chieftain fighting a champion selected by the enemy in single combat.

FREEMEN FARMERS

Many of the Celts were farmers and practised mixed farming, that is they raised cattle and grew crops. In some areas, keeping cattle became more important than the cultivation of cereals. The Celts had iron tools which cleared land more easily than the wooden implements of earlier times. They lived in small farms with square fields or in settlements of just a few houses. In Britain, many Celtic houses were circular and surrounded by a timber palisade, a kind of wooden fence, which protected the whole village. In some areas, hilltop towns were constructed. These were like forts surrounded by deep ditches, great banks of earth and stone, and walls of wood. In the Celtic world, both farmer and warrior felt insecure and life revolved around attack and defence.

LANDLESS MEN AND SLAVES

In battle, the Celts sometimes took men, women and children prisoner. Often the men were beheaded but some were kept as slaves to be sold and to do the heavy work on the land. Women and children were also used as slaves and worked on the farms. These people were landless, that is they owned nothing.

Colour this picture of a hillfort using crayons or felt tipped pens.

INVADERS OR SETTLERS?

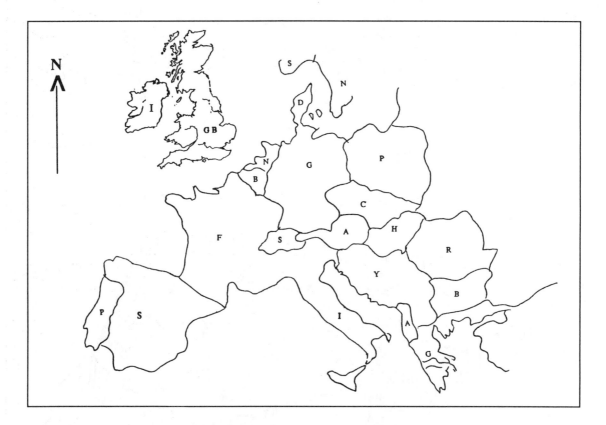

Name the countries on the map which the Celts invaded or in which they settled.

Celtic culture first appeared in Britain between 1000 BC and 500 BC. Tribes first occupied most of Britain south of the Scottish Highlands. The tribes best known to the Romans were the Trinovantes, the Catuvellauni, the Iceni, the Silures, the Ordovices and the Dobunni. Like those in the Bronze Age before them, these peoples built forts with ditches and palisades. Warriors by instinct, the Celts fought not only with their enemies but also raided one another's lands fighting fierce battles with their kinsmen. Combat, often hand to hand and the result of one leader challenging another, usually took place on open ground. Some hillforts, but unfortunately very few, have been the subject of archaeological investigation. Some of the best known include Maiden Castle in Dorset, Chanctonbury Ring in Sussex and Castell Henllys in Cardigan, West Wales.

As well as hillforts, there were several other types of settlement. These included **palisaded enclosures** of various sorts, **unenclosed villages, brochs, duns, raths, crannogs** and many more. The **broch** was made of stone and found in Scotland. Some brochs were massive structures: they looked like stone towers and had complex passages and rooms within them. A broch was easily defended. It had no windows and with its thick wooden door the inhabitants could hold out as long as they had supplies. The **dun** was a small, dry-stone walled enclosure usually occupying about half an acre within which dwellings were defended against attack. The **crannog** was a single homestead built on an artificial island at the edge of a lake and is often described as a bog dwelling.

THINGS TO DO

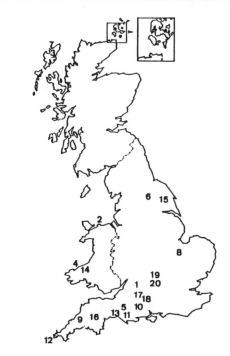

SOME SITES TO VISIT

1. Barbury Castle Hillfort
2. Bronze Age Centre, Great Orme
3. Callanish
4. Castell Henllys Iron Age Fort
5. Cerne Abbas
6. Devil's Arrows
7. Dun Carloway Broch
8. Flag Fen Bronze Age Excavation
9. The Hurlers Bronze Age Site
10. Knowlton
11. Maiden Castle Hillfort
12. Merry Maidens
13. Nine Stones
14. Pentre Ifan
15. Rudston
16. Scorhill
17. Silbury Hill
18. Stonehenge
19. Uffington Hillfort
20. Uffington Hill Figure

Note: This map includes Bronze and Iron Age Sites.

There is little written evidence about prehistoric sites and our knowledge of them depends on information from excavations. Some were inhabited, some were important for religious reasons. There are rings of monoliths (huge, single stones) to puzzle over, hillforts to excavate and figures carved on hillsides for unknown reasons. The origins of many sites are shrouded in myths and legends. Folklore is full of magic, witches, devils, hobgoblins, giants, golden treasures and people turned to salt for all sorts of reasons. What the Celts could not understand or control was attributed to their gods. It is difficult for us to understand how some sites could have been constructed when there were no bulldozers, no mechanical diggers or cranes. It has been suggested that some sites were constructed by beings from outer space or that our ancestors had weird and wonderful magical powers that defied gravity. [Arthur C. Clarke's *A Space Odyssey* suggested that human development was triggered from outer space, the alien presence being associated with a huge monolith, a gigantic, symmetrical slab of stone.] In fact the strongest forces then and now are the determination, persistence, ingenuity and sometimes fanaticism of ordinary human beings.

Visit as many ancient sites as you can. Some have Visitor Centres or Display Centres with exhibitions. When you visit a site take photographs or make drawings, read about its history and make your own history book. Always mark its location on a map.

Make Your Own Site Plan

Draw a diagram of the layout of the site. Often there is a guide book to help you. Look for signs that show where there were walls or ditches. As you walk around the site, imagine what it was like to live there. How would your life then differ from the way you live now?

History

Find out when it was built, by whom and why. Find out who looks after the site today and if there are any other sites like it.

Location

Is the site on a hilltop, near a lake, a river bank or the coast? Why was this particular place chosen? If it was inhabited, consider the advantages and disadvantages of living there and whether it could have been defended against attack. Does it have any religious importance?

Excavations

There may have been archaeological finds. Why are they important and what do they tell you about the site? Was it a settlement, a fortification or a religious site?

Events

Write an account of any important event/s that occurred on the site.

CELTIC LIFE

In spite of the Celt's instinctive love of fighting, they were settlers rather than invaders. They created permanent sites, living in single farmsteads or small settlements or villages. The economy of the Celts was based on mixed farming, rearing beasts and growing crops with grain eventually becoming the more important.

The village was surrounded by a ditch and a palisade, a kind of wooden fence, as a form of defence against attack. Inside, was a cluster of circular wooden houses with thatched roofs. The wooden walls were covered with daub (a mixture of clay, grass and animal dung) to make them weatherproof. Between the houses and off the ground were square-shaped, wooden granaries built on stilts and wooden racks on which hay or fodder was placed to dry in the sun. They also stored food and fodder in underground pits sealed by clay lids. They had ovens for drying and roasting grain. Food and fertilizer were carried in carts.

It was fairly dark inside a roundhouse with warmth and light provided by a fire in the centre. Smoke escaped from this central hearth through the thatched roof or sometimes there was a hole in the roof. The floor was swept regularly and skins were used as mats. Furniture was basic with low, wooden tables, stools and wooden platforms covered with skins for beds.

Most wives and children were used to working with their hands and it was not unusual for there to be a vertical loom with a row of heavy weights on a side wall of the roundhouse.

The Celts were skilled ironworkers and their iron tools meant the farmers could work the land better than earlier people. Modern excavators have found axes, billhooks, adzes, saws, sickles, files and harrows all made of iron. For ploughing, the Celts used wooden ards but sometimes these had iron sheaths.

The chief and his family usually lived in a large roundhouse a little apart from the others and with its own palisade. His weapons and body armour for battle would be kept inside while his decorated war chariot drawn by several ponies and their trappings would be kept outside or stabled.

Women were respected in Celtic society and some became tribal leaders. In Britain, one woman ruler Boudicca (Boadicea), Queen of the Iceni tribe in East Anglia, led a revolt against the Romans in AD 61 which was nearly successful.

The Celts liked eating meats and reared cows, sheep and pigs. Their favourite meat seems to have been pork and choice cuts of roast boar were kept for leaders and heroes. Excavation of graves has shown that joints of pork or even a whole boar were buried with dead warriors to provide the first feast in the underworld. The Celts grew a variety of crops including wheat and barley. They ate porridge and cereals were used to make bread and in stews.

The Celts loved feasting, eating, drinking, talking, singing and gambling with dice made of bone, often over several days to celebrate victories and to reward warriors for success. A boar would be roasted on a wrought iron spit and food prepared in large cauldrons or stone-built tubs with iron hoops and bronze bindings. The lower classes drank mead and cider and wheaten beer called cornia prepared with honey and beer. The Greeks and Romans were impressed by the amount these warriors could drink. After the feasts and strong drink, they often slept where they fell. Aristocratic Celts drank wine neat, to the disgust of the Greeks and Romans who diluted their liquor with water.

Find ten differences between these pictures of Celtic women preparing food inside a roundhouse.
Colour the pictures using crayons or felt tipped pens.

CELTIC CUSTOMS AND SUPERSTITIONS

Information about Celtic customs comes from ancient writings, archaeological excavations (digging up and discovering Celtic sites) and objects they made.

SACRIFICES

Sometimes the bodies of people and objects used for sacrifices to please the gods do not decay but are preserved in the soil or wherever they lie. When these remains are examined by experts, archaeologists and historians, they give valuable information about Celtic customs and beliefs. The Celts often threw victims and prized objects into lakes, bogs and rivers to please their gods. Thus, a neck ring and a boat both made of gold were part of a number of such objects found at Broighter in north-west Ireland. A series of objects was also found in a marsh near the lake at Llyn Cerrig Bach on the Isle of Môna now called Anglesey.

Similarly, the corpse of an Iron Age man was found in a peat bog at Tollund in the Jutland area of Denmark. Discovered in 1950 the man had been put to death probably as a fertility sacrifice to the Goddess of the Earth. Strangled with a leather thong, 'Tollund Man 'was not alone and other bodies, both male and female, were found in the same area. They had been put to death by various methods including hanging, by having their throats cut, by being drowned or buried alive.

SYMBOLS

The Celts believed that some objects such as a torc or ceremonial necklace or neck ring gave them power and protected them from danger. [Today, a crown is seen as a symbol of authority or power and officals such as mayors sometimes wear 'chains of office' around their necks. People also keep charms to bring them luck.]

GODS AND GODDESSES

The Celts believed in many gods and goddesses and that these controlled everything from the weather, a good or bad harvest and fertility to success in battle. They believed that these gods could change shape and take the form of anything in the natural world. They were often thought to be half-animal or half-human, for example, Cernunnos, the horned god. The Celts also believed in the importance of three (the trinity) and some gods were believed to have three heads.

WARRIORS

These men had armour, helmet and shields and went into battle well equipped. Some warriors were used as shock troops - they stripped naked before going into battle believing their nudity would terrify their enemies and give them supernatural powers. Some smeared their blonde hair with chalk-wash to make it look brighter and drew it up into spikes to make their appearance more awesome.

FOES

Celts believed that the head contained the soul and cut off the heads of their enemies. Skulls were kept in pots (in cedar oil), put on poles and (in France in one case) incorporated into a temple doorway.

RITUAL MASSACRES

The Romans declared that the Celts took part in ritual killings. This was probably propaganda and there is no evidence that such massacres were widespread. However, human sacrifices did occur, carried out by Druids (magicians or priests) in ceremonies to please the gods. The Druids decided when these should take place and where, usually in dark groves which they claimed were sacred.

Colour this picture of Celts attacking a hillfort. Use crayons or felt tipped pens.
There are ten objects hidden in the picture. Find a mirror, a necklace, a pin, a torque,
an armband, a bracelet, a brooch, mistletoe, a ring, a god.

CELTS

OAK TREE GROVES

These were favourite places for ceremonies, especially religious ones with people and animals being used. Some plants were believed to have magical powers. Mistletoe was thought to have such powers and people chosen to undergo torture or sacrifice were given mistletoe berries before their ordeal to dull their senses.

SPRINGS

The Celts found spring water fascinating. It often contained substances which had healing properties and the Celts looked on springs and rivers as female gods. They offered wooden carvings of the diseased part of a person's body to these goddesses hoping for a cure. Carvings of eyes, hands, heads, legs and internal organs have been found in springs and at the source of rivers.

GRAVES

The Celts believed in ritual burials and buried things used by the dead in life or likely to be needed by the deceased in the afterlife. Some burials examined have contained a four-wheeled wagon on which the dead person was placed. One of the most important finds was a tomb at Vix, Châtillon-sur-Seine, France, discovered in 1953. This burial chamber contained the skeleton of a woman who died when she was about 30 and was surrounded by jewellery, bracelets, torques, brooches, a necklace and a golden diadem which had been buried with her.

FESTIVALS

The calendar was regulated by the druids and calculated using the movement of the moon. Time was measured by the number of nights that passed and the times of festivals could be fixed in the year. Such festivals were celebrated by eating and drinking to excess. Greek writers record that the Celts sat on the floor on skins or dried grass and the food was placed on low, wooden tables. There were four major festivals in the Celtic calendar, the Samain, Imbolc, Beltine and Lughnasa.

SAMAIN OR SAMHAIN (31st October to 1st November)
This was the beginning of the Celtic year. It was the festival of the dead when the barriers between man and the supernatural were believed to disappear and people from the spirit world could be seen by people on earth. It was believed to be a time of great danger. (Modern equivalent: All Souls'/All Saints'/Martinmas.)

IMBOLC (1st. February)
This was the time of fertility and fruitfulness, the time, for example, when lambs are born. (Modern equivalent St Brigid's/Candlemas.)

BELTINE (BELTANE or BELTAINE) (1st. May)
This was the festival of hope and optimism celebrated with feasting and sacrifices to the gods. Fires were lit and cattle driven between them as a purification rite. It was a time of rejoicing by people thankful to have survived the winter, a time to celebrate the fertility of crops and the birth of young animals. (Modern equivalent might be Whitsun.)

LUGHNASA (LUGNASADH) (1st. August)
Festival of the god Lugh. This celebrated a successful harvest and the rearing of stock. (Modern equivalent Lammas/Harvest festival.)

PUZZLES

1. Which path must the warrior follow to get to his roundhouse?

2. Which piece has broken off the cauldron?

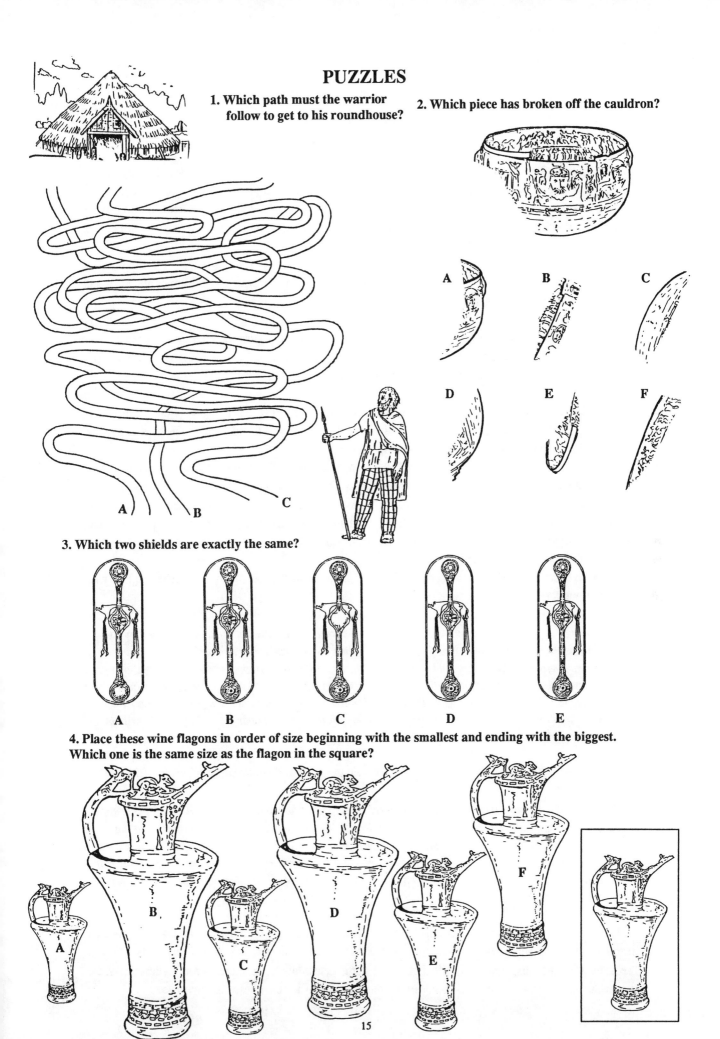

A   B   C

D   E   F

A   B   C

3. Which two shields are exactly the same?

A   B   C   D   E

4. Place these wine flagons in order of size beginning with the smallest and ending with the biggest. Which one is the same size as the flagon in the square?

A   B   C   D   E   F

WARRIORS

The Greek writer Strabo said of the Celts, *The whole nation . . . is war-mad, both high spirited and ready for battle, but otherwise simple and not uncultured.* He related how a warrior wore a long sword fastened on the right side and a long shield. He also carried the 'madaris', a kind of javelin, a wooden weapon to throw at the enemy in battle. Some of the javelins were made with a straight head whilst some were twisted with breaks so that the weapon not only cut but also tore the flesh of the enemy.

To protect himself a warrior carried an oval-shaped shield in the left hand which was big enough to cover most of his body. He also wore a helmet probably made of leather and decorated with animals and birds and sometimes with the horn of an animal. Diodorus Siculus says of these helmets,

> *On their heads they wore bronze helmets which possess projecting figures lending the appearance of enormous stature to the warrior. In some cases horns form one piece with the helmet while in other cases it is the relief figures on the fore parts of birds or quadrupeds.*

Warriors were very superstitious. Some fought in the nude believing that this gave them supernatural protection. Many decorated their bodies blue with a vegetable dye, woad, and coated their hair with chalk wash drawing it up into spikes to give them a terrifying appearance.

Celtic warriors also believed that noise could frighten their opponents. They yelled, beat the sides of their carts and wagons and blew war trumpets. *Their trumpets,* wrote Diodorus, *are of a peculiar barbaric kind. They blow into them and produce a harsh sound which suits the tumult of war.* The trumpets, called carnyx, were long and crowned with animals. The Celts were great psychologists, attempting to frighten their opponents into submission before battle started and carrying out all the superstitions needed to have the support of the gods on their side.

Diodorus described the general war preparations, the cavalry and chariots and the overall battle plans with nobles and supporters,

> *They bring . . . as their attendants free men, chosen from among the poorer class, whom they use as charioteers and shield bearers in battle . . . When the armies are drawn up . . . they are wont to advance before the battle-line and to challenge the bravest of their opponents to single combat, at the same time brandishing before them their arms so as to terrify their foe. And when someone accepts their challenge to battle, they loudly recite the deeds of valour of their ancestors and proclaim their own valorous quality, at the same time abusing and making little of their opponent and generally attempting to rob him beforehand of his fighting spirit.*

The historian, Polybius, described the battle between the Celts and the Romans in Tuscany 225 BC:

> *The Romans . . . were terrified by the fire order of the Celtic host and the dreadful din, for there were innumerable horn blowers and trumpeters, and the whole army was shouting their war cries at the same time: there was such a tumult of sound that it seemed that . . . all the country round had got a voice and caught up the cry. Very terrifying too were the appearance and gestures of all the naked warriors in front, all in the prime of life and finely built men, and all in the leading companies richly adorned with gold torques and armlets.*

The Celts believed that the head contianed the soul, the centre of the emotions and life itself. It was their custom to cut off the heads of their enemies and to ride home with them strapped on the necks of their horses. The heads were then displayed in the tribal home for stangers to admire. The more important the enemy, the greater the value of the head and the heads of the most distinguished enemies were preserved.

Colour this picture of a Celtic Warrior. Use crayons or felt tipped pens.

ART, CLOTHES AND JEWELLERY

Artistically, the Celts were very talented and they loved to make beautiful things. By the 7th. century BC, they had learnt all the skills needed to work bronze and knew how to extract copper and tin. They had also learnt to extract and forge iron, and had mastered the techniques of using graphite and haematite to decorate pottery. They were also able to use materials like gold, silver, coral, amber and glass to make luxury objects. One writer records that in short, *the surviving material remains of Celtic culture show that society was endowed with technology and the craft skills unsurpassed in Europe until the eighteenth century AD.*

ART

One of the most important features was that they used their art on everyday objects, they united the beautiful and the practical. There are a series of styles.

    1. From the end of the Bronze Age to the Hallstatt period.

    2. The La Tène period.

    3. Post La Tène period - Britain.

    4. Irish period.

The following are some of the treasures found in various parts of the world.

The Basse-Yutz Flagons
These are a pair of bronze wine flagons dating from the 4th. century BC. Found at Moselle in eastern France, they are decorated with a number of animals with ducks on the spout.

The Gundestrup Cauldron
This is a silver-plated bronze cauldron measuring 27 inches (68 cm) across. Discovered at Gundestrup in Denmark in 1891, it is richly decorated on the outside with carvings of different gods and on the inside with scenes from Celtic mythology.

The Desborough Mirror
From the 1st. century BC until 43 AD the Celts made a variety of bronze mirrors with elaborate handles and engravings on their backs. This mirror was discovered at Desborough in Northamptonshire in 1908. It was made in the 1st. century AD.

The Witham Shield
This was found in the River Witham near Lincoln and has embossed Celtic patterns and fine engraving. The figure of a boar was part of the earlier decoration but this has now disappeared.

The Battersea Horned Helmet
The bronze horned helmet and bronze shield found in the Thames at Battersea are two further examples of Celtic workmanship.

One of the Basse-Yutz Flagons

The Desborough Mirror

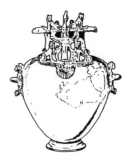

A Bronze Hydria

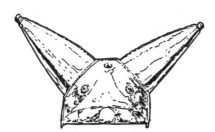

The Battersea Horned Helmet

The Gundestrup Cauldron

The Witham Shield

Celtic women wore long dresses down to their ankles. Their skirts were gathered in the middle and held up by leather belts to which a number of ornaments might be attached. There were no buttons and clothes were fastened by different types of pins and brooches.

Colour these pictures using crayons or felt tipped pens.

Drawings not to scale.

CLOTHES

The Celts were concerned about their personal appearance. Very few were fat which was socially unacceptable and women used mirrors, make-up and tweezers to pluck their eyebrows. Unfortunately, very little is known about the clothes worn by the Celts because few have survived. A chieftain would have worn a tunic, plaid trousers and cloak. These were brightly coloured and it is possible that Scottish tartans continue this tradition. Leather belts were popular from earliest times and brooches (fibulae) were used to fasten cloaks at the breast or on the shoulder. Such a chief would also have worn a sword or dagger, a torc around his neck and gold bracelets or arm rings. In battle such a chief would have worn a bronze helmet with a tall crest giving him extra height. In this way the Celts towered over their enemy in battle giving them a psychological advantage. One Greek traveller wrote *They use amazing colours, brightly dyed shirts with flowing patterns and trousers called breeches . . .* and *Their nobles let their moustaches grow so long that they hide their mouths and, when they eat, get entangled in their food . . .*

Men wore a loose tunic and plaid trousers and were fond of bright colours and patterned cloth. The women wore long dresses down to their ankles. Their skirts were gathered in the middle and held up by leather belts to which a number of ornaments might be attached. There were no buttons and clothes were fastened by different types of pins and brooches.

Dio Cassius described Boudicca (Boadicea), the Queen of the Iceni thus: *She was huge of frame, terrifying of aspect and with a harsh voice. A great mass of bright red hair fell to her knees: she wore a great twisted golden torc, and a tunic of many colours, over which was a thick mantle, fastened by a brooch. Now she grasped a spear, to strike fear into all who watched her.*

JEWELLERY

Celtic men and women loved to wear jewellery. Numerous ornamental pins and brooches have been found by archaeologists. These were often decorated with human and animal faces. Also torcs worked in brass, silver or gold and with their ends formed into human heads and lion masks have been discovered. Gold bracelets or arm bands were popular among the nobility and fine metalwork including coloured enamel highlights was used in many of the pieces. Sunflower pins were also worn - these had carefully crafted heads which shone brightly on the wearer's clothes.

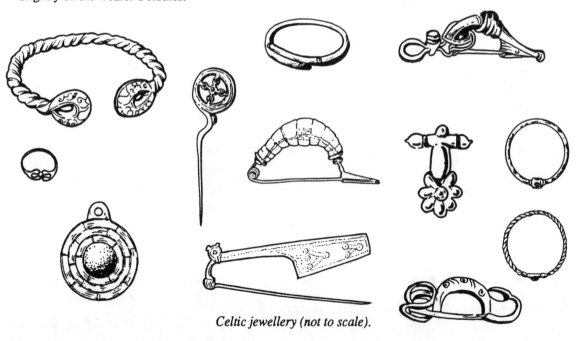

Celtic jewellery (not to scale).

Colour this picture showing the Celts working with iron. Use crayons or felt tipped pens.

RELIGION

The druids were the priests of the Celts, the wise men of their society. They were healers, teachers, musicians, poets and judges. Nothing was written down, Celtic was not a written language and so they were responsible for the care of all knowledge and for passing it on. Amongst the things they had to remember were ritual procedures, magic formulae, prayers, medical knowledge, folk history, law and genealogies.Caesar describes their duties as, *they officiate at the worship of the gods, regulate public and private sacrifices and give rulings on all religious questions* . . . Druids were exempt from taxes and military service and had to memorise all the teachings of the tribes.

At the core of their teachings was the belief that the soul did not die but passed into another body. Because of this, the Celts had little fear of death and had a strong belief in an afterlife. Neither did they believe in sin or punishment.

One of the rituals practised by the druids is described by Pliny. He tells that mistletoe, well known for its healing properties, was considered to be particularly potent if found growing near an oak tree and cut in a special way. First, two white bulls were brought to the place. Then a white-robed druid cut the mistletoe with a golden sickle and the branch was caught in a white robe by those below. The bulls were then sacrificed while prayers were said to the god. It was believed that mistletoe cut in this way and taken in a drink could make barren animals fertile and was an antidote for all poisons.

It has been established from archaeological evidence that the Celts worshipped more than 400 different gods. There was no one god common to all the peoples and it is possible that every Celtic family had its own god whilst believing in the existence of hundreds of others. As far as the Celts were concerned, the supernatural was everywhere. The spirits were in trees, mountains and rivers, strangely shaped rocks and in marshes and bogs. Gods were responsible for the weather and the seasons and they controlled the natural world of which men were a part. If there was a disaster such as famine or disease, it happened because the gods were angry and had to be placated or appeased. A sacrifice or offering was needed to make the gods look on the people more favourably.

Some animals such as bulls, boars, dogs and birds were sacred to the Celts. They may not have believed these animals were gods, but the creatures were used in religious rituals.

The trinity was an important idea and often their gods were represented with three heads (tricephalos). The idea of the *Three Mothers* appears in nearly all parts of the Celtc world and occasionally the sacred bull appears with three horns instead of the usual two.

Horned gods were common. Cernunnos was one of these and was depicted in human form with the horned head of a deer. The main gods were undoubtedly the earth mother-goddess and the tribal father god. The great male god, the god on whom all tribal gods were based, was Dugdá. Translated this means *the god good at everything*. His female counterpart was the Mórrigan described as *the great queen, the mother goddess and the goddess of fertility*. The relationship between these gods explained everything, good and evil, bravery and fear, life and death.

Amongst the important individual gods were

Lug or Lugh, probably a fertility god,
Epona, a horse goddess,
Matres or Matronae, mother goddesses and
Sulis, a female god endowed with powers of healing the sick.

Many references to religion do not deal with gods at all but with the importance of places that were special to the Celts. These were their sanctuaries, sacred woods, sacred lakes, sacred bogs and swamps being the most important. They worshipped their gods not in temples but in these sacred places. There were many such places

Join the dots and find a sacred animal then colour this picture showing the druids cutting mistletoe. Use crayons or felt tipped pens.

including a wood near Marseilles, the source of the rivers Marne and Seine. It was at these sanctuaries that vows were taken and sacrifices made. At the mouth of the Seine, for example, excavations have revealed about 190 pieces of wood carvings with more than 20 complete statues dating from the middle of the 1st. century AD. A great hoard was discovered at Llyn Cerrig Bach in Anglesey, North Wales in 1943. It consisted of many weapons, chariot furniture, slave chains with collars attached, cauldrons and fragments of bronze. The find is believed to consist of sacrificial offerings made between the mid 2nd. century BC to the middle of the 1st. century AD.

Animal and human sacrifices were made at these sites too. Criminals were preferred as sacrifices but if there were not enough, other humans were used to make up the numbers. The Romans exaggerated the extent of such sacrifices. Caesar asserts in a typical piece of Roman propaganda, *Some tribes have colossal images made of wickerwork, the limbs of which they fill with living men: they are then set on fire, and the victims are burnt to death.* There is no doubt that human sacrifices were performed and were of considerable ritual importance. It has been argued that such human sacrifices were practised *more commonly at times of communal danger or stress, rather than as part of regular ritual observance.*

In some parts of the world, the Celts dug deep shafts and it has been suggested that they were trying to reach the underworld.

THINGS TO DO

MAKE A BOOKMARK

Cut a piece of card 20 cm x 4cm. Use the Celtic design on page 29 to make a bookmark.

MAKE A CELTIC BROOCH

Trace the small fantastic bird design on page 26. Colour it with gold and silver paints or sequins and glitter. Paste it to a piece of cardboard and tape a safety pin to the back.

MAKE A PAPERWEIGHT

Find a smooth, large, beach pebble, or one with an interesting shape. Paint a Celtic pattern or a warrior's head on it.

MAKE A DESK-TIDY

Cover several cardboard rolls (from toilet rolls, cooking foil, kitchen rolls) with different patterns. Glue them together and then on to a circle of cardboard to make a holder for pens and pencils.

MAKE A TOY BOX

Choose a strong cardboard box. Decorate it with drawings from the pictures in this book.

Use crayons or felt tipped pens to colour this picture of a Wickerman filled with humans about to be sacrificed to the gods.

(This wooden monster did not exist but was probably invented by the Romans to discredit the Celts.)

THE 'HEROIC' AGE

In 1858 an important discovery was made at La Tène, on the banks of Lake Neuchatel in Switzerland. There, large quantities of Iron Age metalwork were found including swords, spears, shields, horse gear, tools of all kinds, jewellery, ornaments, coins and many other objects. At first, it was thought that these items were thrown into the lake to appease the gods but later research suggests that the site was probably a domestic and industrial settlement on dry land which was suddenly flooded. The La Tène culture which began about 600 BC was regarded as the finest period of Celtic domination, their *heroic age*. They expanded into the Balkans, Greece and Asia Minor, they sacked Rome about 390 BC and Delphi around 279 BC. Before the La Tène culture was over, the Celts had penetrated into Britain and Ireland.

Artistically too, La Tène culture contributed to luxury items in weapons and jewellery such as many brooches decorated with human and animal heads. Later, in the second half of the 4th. century, enamel, first in red and then in other colours, was added to the bronze work. Ducks and birds were included in pottery items and in Britain bronze mirrors were made with patterns cut into their surfaces.

THINGS TO DO

Trace and colour these pieces. Then cut them out and put them together to make this fantastic bird.

26

A CELTIC QUIZ

1. Where did the word 'Celt' come from and what did it mean?

2. When did the Celts first arrive in Britain?

3. Where did the word 'Britons' come from?

4. What part of Britain did the Celts occupy?

5. What shape were Celtic housets?

6. What were Celtic houses made of?

7. How were Celtic houses heated?

8. What is the name of the fence around a Celtic settlement?

9. The Celts were important because they were the first invaders to settle in Britain. What was their main occupation?

10. What did Celtic farmers do?

11. What is an ard?

12. Name the five levels of Celtic society.

13. What was the name given to Celtic priests?

14. Stone and bronze were used before Celtic times. What new material did the Celts learn to extract and use?

15. Celtic warriors decorated their bodies with a blue dye. From which plant was this obtained?

16. The Celts had no buttons to fasten their clothes. What did they use?

17. Give the name of the Celtic long trumpet.

18. Name(a) the bull or ram horned god, (b) the horse goddess.

19. Name the plant associated with sacrifices and which the Celts thought sacred.

20. Name the four main Celtic festivals.

21. Identify the following objects.

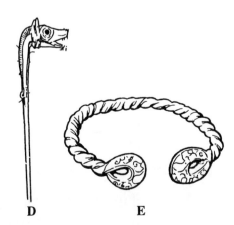

A   B   C   D   E

THE CELTIC LEGACY

In some parts of the world especially in the Highlands and Islands of Scotland, Ireland, the Isle of Man, Wales, Cornwall and Britanny, Celtic culture lives on. These peoples are proud of their heritage and such traditions remain influential. Folk customs have been carefully preserved with 'modern' culture imposed on them. In Wales, for example, the Eisteddfod was revived in 1789 and has continued ever since: the contestants and audiences are never allowed to forget their Celtic ancestry. In Scotland, there are the Highland Games, gatherings featuring contests of skill and strength such as tossing the caber, throwing the hammer, folk dancing and playing the bagpipes. In the Highlands and Islands, the clan system is important and relates back to the Celtic social system.

The traditions remain also in the languages spoken. Irish Gaelic is taught in all Ireland's schools and is spoken by just over a million people although in areas other than those of the north and west it is still very much a second language. Scottish Gaelic was the everyday language of Scotland until the late 17th century when English became the language of education and government. It has enjoyed a revival in recent years and is spoken by some 69,000 Scots. Breton, spoken by the people of Brittany, is quite close to Welsh. Over 300,000 speak the language but unfortunately most of the speakers are aged and the language could decline quickly. In the Isle of Man, Manx is spoken for ceremonial occasions like the meetings of Tynwald and attempts are being made to revive the language for more everyday use. In Cornwall, the language is all but dead although there are some signs of an academic revival. In Wales, over half a million speak Welsh especially in the north and west of the Principality. Welsh has been given equal status with English and is used extensively in street and road signs, and in official documents which are printed in both languages. Wales has a TV and a radio station devoted to its own language and Welsh was saved from extinction in the south partly by the policy of providing bilingual schools in the area. The National Curriculum states that all children should have instruction in the Welsh language.

In all the Celtic lands, evidence of earlier times remain in street, road and place names. *Ewenny* in Glamorgan, for example, comes from *Aventia,* the name of a Celtic goddess, *Denbigh* in Clwyd is derived from the Celtic *dounon* meaning an enclosed safe place; *Clarach* in Dyfed has the Celtic suffix *-ach* meaning water and *claer* meaning *bright and clear*. Individual names throughout the 'Celtic fringe' also have ancient origins. Celtic Christian names survive in names like Brian, Donald, Emlyn, Deirdre, Morwenna and Muriel.

THINGS TO DO

Trace these Celtic patterns, colour them and use them to decorate a frame for a picture or photograph.

GLOSSARY

Als A Danish island famous as the site of a Celtic discovery. A long boat, 16 metres long and big enough to carry 20 men, was dug out of a bog at Hjortopring. War equipment found included 150 wooden shields, 169 spears and 8 iron swords.

Ard Simple Celtic plough.

Aristotle A great Greek philosopher who wrote about the Celts in 330 BC. Others who wrote about them are **Cornelius Tacitus** (14 AD - 96 AD), **Julius Caesar** (died 44 BC), **Livy** (1st. century BC), **Pliny the Elder** (AD 79), **Polybius** (2nd. century BC) and **Strabo** (1st. Century BC). Much of what is known about the Celts is based on these writings.

Beltane One of the Celtic festivals which began on 1st. May. Three other major festivals were **Samain, Imbolc** and **Lughnasa.**

Boudicca (or Boudica or Boadicea) Queen of the Iceni, the Celtic tribe who settled in Eastern Britain.

Bracae The name given to the breeches worn by the Celts.

Broch A tall, circular stone house which some Celts built to protect themselves from attack.

Carnyx A type of tall trumpet with an animal's head at the end. Usually used in battles.

Cernunnos A Celtic god who is shown as human and squatting but with a horned head.

Cornia A type of beer made from wheat and prepared with honey.

Dagdá One of the most important Celtic gods. This is the male god, *good at everything.*

Daub A mixture of clay, straw, animal hair and dung used on the walls of Celtic wooden houses to weatherproof them.

Druids The 'wise men' of Celtic society who were priests, teachers, judges and healers.

Epona A Celtic god, a horse goddess usually shown sitting on a horse or accompanied by a foal.

Fibulae Brooches used to fasten cloaks at the chest or on the shoulder.

Gae A heavy spear used by the Celts.

Hallstatt The earliest phase of the European Iron Age - and the first phase of Celtic culture - named after a place in Austria.

La Tène A later phase of the European Iron Age (the 5th. century AD onwards) and a later phase of Celtic culture named after a discovery on the banks of Lake Neuchâtel in Switzerland.

Llyn Cerrig Bach A site in North Wales made famous when Celtic finds were discovered there in 1943. The collection includes swords, spears, shields, chariot and harness trappings, ironworkers' tools, trumpets, cauldrons and a slave chain.

Madaris One of the weapons used by the Celts. It was very much like a javelin.

Roundhouse A name for the typical Celtic house built in Western Europe, particularly Britain.

Sauterrain (fogan in Cornwall and **weem** in Scotland) A type of cave or underground structure which may have had ritual functions or may have been used by the Celts in times of danger.

Torc or torque A type of necklace worn by both men and women in Celtic times. Some of the torcs found have been made of gold, silver and brass.

Woad A blue dye obtained from leaves and used by the Celts to decorate their bodies.

PUZZLES

1. The following are clues to words hidden in the word square. Can you find them?
The words may be in the square backwards, upside down or diagonally and any letter may be used more than once.

1. Worn on the head.
2. Worn around the neck.
3. Drunk by the Celts.
4. Celtic priests.
5. Blown in battle.
6. Celts were the first to extract this metal.
7. Brave Celt who fought battles.
8. Used to keep clothing together.
9. Carried for protection in a battle.
10. A sign of bad luck or good luck.
11. Long weapon.
12. City sacked by the Celts.
13. Blue vegetable dye.
14. Head of a settlement.
15. Celts put this on their hair before battle.
16. Simple plough.
17. To rear cattle, especially young ones.
18. Used to weatherproof Celtic houses.
19. Lays eggs.
20. Defensive fence around a Celtic settlement.
21. Most Celts were . . . .
22. Battles.
23. Worshipped by the Celts.
24. Makes honey.
25. Clan.
26. Celtic home.
27. Decorative pin.
28. Father.
29. Celts built this at the top of a hill.
30. Used to travel on water.
31. Boiled boar.
32. Grain was laid on trays to . . .
33. Fodder from grass.
34. Part of daub.
35. To chafe.
36. Group of cattle.
37. Bright, decorative colour.
38. Used to catch fish.
39. Celts lived a long time . . .
40. Not night.
41. One more than nine.
42. Useful if 30 sinks.

T	T	R	I	B	E	H	W	O	A	D	B	R
R	R	O	T	O	R	C	A	A	A	R	R	O
O	U	M	E	A	D	B	R	Y	S	E	O	U
F	M	E	M	T	R	P	R	E	D	H	O	N
E	P	N	L	E	U	D	I	R	U	B	C	D
I	E	E	E	B	I	R	O	N	N	U	H	H
H	T	D	H	T	D	W	R	O	G	A	S	O
C	H	A	L	K	S	H	I	E	L	D	T	U
G	O	D	S	P	A	L	I	S	A	D	E	S
T	F	A	R	M	E	R	S	R	A	W	N	E

2. Who am I?

My first is in war but not in battle.
My second is in palisade but not in fence.
My third is in fire and also in water.
My fourth is in spear and also in fear.
My fifth is in shield but not in sword.
My sixth is in foe but not in enemy.
My last is found twice in chariot.
My whole is a hero of the Celts.

3. The following are the names of things you might find in a Celtic settlement but the letters are muddled up. What are they?

ARAYNGR, YETROTP, HLGUPO, TPIS, RATC, ETSILOMET, OMLO, PRASE, RDLUNOAC, RTHOACI.

4. How many words can you make from the letters in

A CELTIC SETTLEMENT?

(30 words good, 60 words very good, 100 words excellent.)

ANSWERS

Page 8

Page 11

Page 31

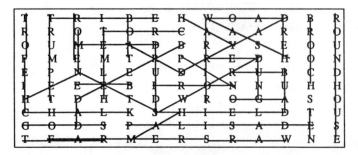

Page 15

1 C. 2 D. 3 B and D. 4 A C E F D B. Flagon C is the same size as the one in the square.

Page 27 Quiz

1. From the Greek 'Keltoi' meaning a war-like people.
2. About 500 BC or before.
3. From the Celtic tribe known as Prythons.
4. Most of Britain south of the Scottish Highlands.
5. Usually round.
6. Wood, reeds, hardened dung and mud with thatched roofs of reed and straw.
7. By a fire in the centre of the floor.
8. Palisade.
9. Mixed farming.
10. Grew crops and reared cattle.
11. A simple plough.
12. King, druids, chiefs, freemen/farmers and landless/slaves.
13. Druids.
14. Iron.
15. Woad plant.
16. Brooches and pins.
17. Carnyx.
18. (a) Cernunnos (b) Epona.
19. Mistletoe.
20. Beltane, Imbolc, Lughnasa, Samain.
21. **A** Wine flagon, **B** Shield, **C** Pin, **D** Long Trumpet (carnyx), **E** Torc or torque.

Page 31

1. Word square.

1. Helmet.	22. Wars.
2. Torc.	23. Gods.
3. Mead.	24. Bee.
4. Druids.	25. Tribe.
5. Trumpet.	26. Roundhouse.
6. Iron.	27. Brooch.
7. Warrior.	28. Dad.
8. Pin.	29. Fort.
9. Shield.	30. Boat.
10. Omen.	31. Ham.
11. Sword.	32. Dry.
12. Rome.	33. Hay.
13. Woad.	34. Dung.
14. Chief.	35. Rub.
15. Chalkwash.	36. Herd.
16. Ard.	37. Red.
17. Breed.	38. Nets.
18. Daub.	39. Ago.
19. Hen.	40. Day.
20. Palisade.	41. Ten.
21. Farmers.	42. Raft.

2. WARRIOR.

3. GRANARY, POTTERY, PLOUGH, SPIT, CART, MISTLETOE, LOOM, SPEAR, CAULDRON, CHARIOT.